The First Christmas

Written by
VIVIAN FRENCH

Illustrated by
JANE CHAPMAN

Early Learning Centre   WALKER BOOKS

A long time ago God called for the angel Gabriel, and gave him a very special message to deliver. God told Gabriel to go to a city called Nazareth and find the house where a young woman called Mary lived.

When Mary saw the angel she
was frightened, but Gabriel told
her not to be afraid.

"God has sent me," he said. "God
has chosen you to be the mother
of His baby. He will be a wonderful
baby and his name will be Jesus."

Mary was surprised, but
she smiled at the angel.
"I'm happy to do whatever
God wants," she said.

Mary had promised to marry
a carpenter called Joseph. Joseph
heard that Mary was going to have
a baby, and he began to worry
about what he should do.

God knew that Joseph was
worrying, so He sent an angel
to visit him. When the angel
arrived, Joseph was fast asleep,
so the angel slipped into
Joseph's dream.

"Don't worry any more," the
angel told him. "This is God's
baby and when he is born you
are to call him Jesus."

Mary and Joseph were waiting for the baby to be born when an order came from the emperor.

Everyone was to pay him some money. It didn't matter if they were old or ill or even if they were about to have a baby – the emperor said they must go at once to the city from which their family came, to make the payment.

Joseph's family came from Bethlehem, so he and Mary had to pack their things and leave Nazareth.

As it was nearly time for the baby to be born, they travelled very slowly along the road to Bethlehem.

When Mary and Joseph reached Bethlehem, they found many other people there. Grandfathers and grandmothers, uncles and aunts, fathers and mothers and sisters and brothers and cousins; everyone had come to pay the emperor the money he wanted.

All the places to stay were full. Mary and Joseph knocked on every door, but the answer was always the same – no room, no room. The only place they could find to stay was a stable, where the animals were kept.

While they were there, the baby Jesus was born. Mary wrapped him carefully and laid him in a manger full of soft hay.

The stable was not very far from some fields where shepherds were looking after their sheep. It was night time, but suddenly the sky lit up. High above them was an angel. The shepherds were scared, but the angel told them not to be afraid.

He said, "I bring you wonderful news! Tonight in Bethlehem the saviour of the world is born!" And he told the shepherds how they could find the baby, safely wrapped and lying in a manger.

Then, just as suddenly as the first angel had come, the whole sky was full of angels singing, "Glory to God in the highest, and on earth peace, goodwill towards men."

When the angels had flown back into heaven, the shepherds rubbed their eyes.

"Let's go to Bethlehem!" they said. And they left their sheep and hurried off to look for the stable.

There they found Mary and
Joseph, and the baby lying in the
manger, just as the angel had said.

It wasn't only the shepherds
who wanted to see the baby Jesus.
A long way away three wise men
saw a star in the Eastern sky. They
knew it was a sign that someone
very important had been born,
and they followed the star until
it came to rest above the stable.

The wise men came inside, and
saw Jesus with his mother, Mary,
and bowed down. They gave
the baby presents of gold and
sweet-smelling spices called
frankincense and myrrh.

And up above the stable all the
angels sang as the star shone down.
The Son of God was born.

For Marcus and Sally
with love
V.F.
For George David
J.C.

Published 1998 exclusively for
Early Learning Centre
South Marston Park
Swindon SN3 4TJ
by Walker Books Ltd
87 Vauxhall Walk
London SE11 5HJ

2 4 6 8 10 9 7 5 3 1

Text © 1998 Vivian French
Illustrations © 1998 Jane Chapman

Printed in Hong Kong

ISBN 0-7445-2929-8